Notes

Story by Josie Stewart and Lynn Salem
Illustrations by Mary Smerillo

I write notes to my Dad all the time.

Then I give my notes to Dad.

When I go out to play, I write a note.

When it's time to go shopping,
I write a note.

When I have a ball game,
I write another note.

Dear Dad,

Please come to
see me play at 6:00.

Your star,
Stevie

**When it's Dad's birthday,
I make cards and cards and cards.**

But, I write the biggest note I can, when I want to tell him...